D0428588

Traveler's

JOURNAL

Traveler's
J O U R N A L

*A place to record
the special memories
that traveling brings.*

BLUEBERRY BOOKS

ISBN 0-8300-0342-8

Traveler's Journal
was prepared and produced by
Tern Enterprises, Inc.
Sagaponack Road
Bridgehampton, New York 11932

Printed and bound in Hong Kong by Leefung-Asco Printers Ltd.

Produced exclusively for
BLUEBERRY BOOKS

The white sails still fly seaward, seaward flying
  Unbroken wings.
And the lost heart stiffens and rejoices
In the lost lilac and the lost sea voices
And the weak spirit quickens to rebel
For the bent goldenrod and the lost sea smell.

— T.S. Eliot

Rates designated "European Plan" include lodging but no meals, although some inns serve a continental breakfast with the European Plan. The "American Plan" covers lodging and three meals. "Modified American Plan" includes lodging and two meals, usually breakfast and dinner. Choose your plan wisely, taking into account both economy and the degree of flexibility you'll desire in planning your days.

. . . .

. . . .

. . . .

. . . .

. . . .

. . . .

. . . .

. . . .

. . . .

. . . .

. . . .

. . . .

. . . .

. . . .

. . . .

. . . .

There is nothing which has yet been contrived by man by which so much happiness is produced as by a good tavern or inn.

—Samuel Johnson

Full-time students 15 years or older may apply for an International Student Identity Card, regardless of their nationality. This card grants discounts at many museums and other cultural sites or events, plus lower rates for some lodgings and means of travel. There are a number of other student cards available to international travelers that grant discounts to various different attractions. When using any student card, be prepared to show further proof of student status.

Travel, in the younger sort, is a part of education; in the elder, a part of experience. He that traveleth into a country before he hath some entrance into the language, goeth to school, and not to travel.
— Sir Francis Bacon

The longest part of the journey is said to be the passing of the gate.

— Marcus Terentius Varro

A journey of a thousand miles must begin with a single step.

— Lao-tzu

If you plan to drive a car in a foreign country, contact its embassy or consulate before you leave home and ask what the regulations are. A U.S. driver's license can be used in most European countries and Britain for up to one year of residence, but some countries also require your license to be translated into their language.

Always read the contract when you rent a car. In many cases, repairs you make to the car without authorization from the rental agency will not be reimbursed. There may be many other restrictions, as well as options regarding your liability for accidents or damage to the vehicle. Rental agencies prefer credit card payments; if you want to pay cash, you will have to leave a substantial deposit.

Farewell, Monsieur Traveler: look you lisp and wear strange suits, disable all the benefits of your own country, be out of love with your nativity, and almost chide God for making you that countenance that you are; or I will scarce think you have swam in a gondola.

— Shakespeare

. . . .

. . . .

. . . .

. . . .

. . . .

. . . .

. . . .

. . . .

. . . .

. . . .

. . . .

. . . .

. . . .

Travel in countries culturally very different from your own brings many joys—and many problems. Be very conscious of your manner and gestures when speaking with people abroad. Many common Western hand gestures are the height of rudeness in the Middle and Far East, and the opposite holds true as well. The best rule in unfamiliar territory is to smile, nod your head, and smile some more.

Much have I traveled in the realms of gold,
And many goodly states and kingdoms seen;
Round many western islands have I been
Which bards in fealty to Apollo hold.

— Keats

Don't try to look too professional with your expensive camera equipment. In many countries, professional photographers are subject to taxes and restrictions the tourist photographer is not. Resist the temptation to show off.

The soul of a journey is liberty, perfect liberty, to think, feel, do just as one pleases.
— William Hazlitt, 1822

. . . .

. . . .

. . . .

. . . .

. . . .

. . . .

. . . .

. . . .

. . . .

. . . .

. . . .

"Glorious starry night!" murmured toad...“The poetry of motion! The real *way to travel! The* only *way to travel! Here today—in next week tomorrow! Villages skipped, towns and cities jumped—always somebody else's horizons! O bliss! O poop-poop! O my! O my!"*

— Kenneth Grahame

I long for Europe of the ancient parapets.
— Arthur Rimbaud

In Austria, three of the most historical and romantic places to stay are the castles Schloss Hotel Durnstein, Faust Schlossl, and Schlosshotel Martinschloss. The oldest castle, 15-century Faust Schlossl, reputedly was built in one night by the Devil as part of his bargain with Faust. The other two castles are equally historic—Durnstein was built in 1632 on the ruins of the castle where Richard the Lionheart was imprisoned, and Martinschloss saw the invention of the underwater torpedo in its swimming pool.

"Family Style Dining" at an inn or lodge indicates that meals are served at one or two seatings, on platters at large tables. Guests are expected to form casual groups, and dine together in a familial atmosphere—children are encouraged to attend. If intimate, private dining is what you prefer, you'll have to go elsewhere.

Oh that I had in the wilderness a lodging place of wayfaring men!

— Jeremiah

To apply for a U.S. passport, you must submit proof of citizenship or nationalization, two identical full-face photographs, and identification. Processing takes from ten days to two weeks, but in special circumstances may be speeded up considerably. If while in a country requiring an entry visa your passport expires, you must re-apply for the visa — it expires along with the passport. You may renew your passport at any U.S. consulate or embassy.

. . . .

. . . .

. . . .

. . . .

. . . .

. . . .

. . . .

. . . .

. . . .

. . . .

. . . .

. . . .

. . . .

Manage your visas with discretion. Although your
own country may not be engaged in hostilities
with any of the countries you visit, many of those
countries are hostile toward each other. No Arab
country will accept a tourist whose passport holds
an Israeli visa. If you plan to visit Israel before
continuing on in the Middle East, ask for your
visa on a separate sheet. This is common practice
in Israel, and well worth the aggravation of being
refused entry into a country you wish to visit.

A particular resort area's "season" is not always its best time of year. Generally, the season is determined by the weather from which tourists are escaping. That means that often the best time to visit a country is not during peak tourist months and therefore can be much less expensive. This is especially true for the Mediterranean and the Caribbean. Check weather statistics for a tourist spot before you decide when to go.

At two hours after midnight appeared the land, at a distance of 2 leagues. They handed all sails and set the treo, which is the mainsail without bonnets, and lay-to waiting for the daylight Friday, when we arrived at an island of the Bahamas that was called in the Indians' tongue Guanahani.
— Christopher Columbus

Pack a few plastic bags to keep dirty or damp clothing and bathing suits separate from other clothes.

Journey all over the universe in a map, without the expense and fatigue of traveling, without suffering the inconveniences of heat, cold, hunger and thirst.

— Cervantes

I never travel without my diary. One should always have something sensational to read on the train.

— Oscar Wilde

Traveling by train is a pleasant option not always considered by Americans; nonetheless, it is becoming an increasingly popular mode of travel inside the United States. Amtrak has limited but very well-serviced routes throughout the U.S. Train travel can be more comfortable and relaxing than driving and is certainly more leisurely than flying, and few major highways are as scenic as Amtrak routes.

Although it is not necessarily unsafe to travel when pregnant, many airlines — and even many countries — hesitate to allow access to women who are eight or nine months pregnant. Airlines may require a doctor's statement that no complications are likely to occur. The problems contingent upon giving birth in a foreign country should be warning enough against international travel after the seventh month of pregnancy.

. . . .

. . . .

. . . .

. . . .

. . . .

. . . .

. . . .

. . . .

. . . .

. . . .

. . . .

The pressurized air in aircraft cabins is often more bothersome to infants and young children than to adults. A baby can be quieted and made more comfortable during liftoff and landing with small drinks of water, which will prevent headaches in adults as well.

*Lump the whole thing! Say that the Creator made
Italy from designs by Michael Angelo!*

— Twain

. . . .

. . . .

. . . .

. . . .

. . . .

. . . .

. . . .

. . . .

. . . .

. . . .

. . . .

. . . .

. . . .

. . . .

. . . .

Italia! O Italia! thou who hast
The fatal gift of beauty.

— Byron

The sea is at its best at London, near midnight,
when you are within the arms of a capacious
chair, before a glowing fire, selecting phases of the
voyages you will never make.
                    — Henry Major Tomlinson, 1912

The oldest continuously operating inn in the U.S. is the Beekman Arms in Rhinebeck, New York. Built at a crossroads in 1700, the Beekman has hosted many famous Americans, from Washington and Lafayette to Roosevelt and the Vanderbilts.

Dining in hotels or inns can be a delightful experience, depending on the atmosphere and the cuisine. As a general rule, those establishments open to the public as well as to overnight guests are better than those for guests only — competition with local restaurants ensures competitive cuisine, service, and prices.

When dining out in rural areas, stick to simple, regional foods, as these will invariably be better than fancy dishes.

. . . .

. . . .

. . . .

. . . .

. . . .

. . . .

. . . .

. . . .

. . . .

. . . .

. . . .

. . . .

. . . .

. . . .

. . . .

One of the most romantic and authentic of hotels in the Deep South is the Hotel Maison de Ville in New Orleans, where Tennessee Williams wrote *A Streetcar Named Desire*. From this vantage point, the mysterious and exciting French Quarter is at hand, as well as the rest of New Orleans.

All educated Americans, first or last, go to Europe.

— Emerson

One of the pleasantest things in the world is going on a journey; but I like to go by myself.
— William Hazlit, 1822

. . . .

. . . .

. . . .

. . . .

. . . .

. . . .

. . . .

. . . .

. . . .

. . . .

. . . .

. . . .

. . . .

The man who goes alone can start today; but he who travels with another must wait till that other is ready.

— Thoreau

There are few comprehensive guides to the B&B's of the U.S. available, as they drop in and out of the market so frequently. When you have decided on a destination, consult the local Chamber of Commerce for B&B's nearby. The Chamber of Commerce cannot give recommendations, however, so you must be prepared for the worst, even though you may end up with new friends.

"B&B," or "Bed and Breakfast," long an institution in Europe, is fast becoming the preferred lodging in the United States. B&B's are usually private homes with accomodation for very small groups, often no more than one couple. The formality or informality of the B&B varies — but be prepared to be made one of the family. B&B hosts often provide the service for the company as much as for the extra money.

The last time I saw Paris, her heart was warm and gay.
I heard the laughter of her heart in every street café.

— Oscar Hammerstein III

One of the most beautiful, and most frequently photographed chateaux of France is the Chateau du Gue'-Péan in the breathtaking Loire Valley. Turreted Norman towers, cobbled courtyards, Renaissance additions, and elements of the Louis XIII style create an almost fairy-tale effect. The residence of many French kings, Gue'-Péan also has hosted great writers, statesmen, and ghosts. Although a private residence, the chateau takes guests for limited stays, and is considered one of the luxury hotels of Europe.

. . . .

. . . .

. . . .

. . . .

. . . .

. . . .

. . . .

. . . .

. . . .

. . . .

. . . .

. . . .

Most Scandinavians speak English, and many Europeans do as well, which makes getting around easier. But it is always wise to know some of the language of the country you plan to visit. It is useful in emergencies, and will help to break down cultural barriers.

And learn, O voyager, to walk
The roll of earth, the pitch and fall
That swings across these trees those stars:
That swings the sunlight up the wall.
— Archibald MacLeish

A single woman traveling in Islam is considered to be immoral and/or insane. In some Arab countries, unaccompanied women are denied entry. Aside from the personal indignation this may cause, it is simply dangerous for women to travel alone through Islam. Harassment, and even abduction, are not uncommon occurrences.

. . . .

. . . .

. . . .

. . . .

. . . .

. . . .

. . . .

. . . .

. . . .

. . . .

. . . .

. . . .

. . . .

. . . .

When entering an Islamic mosque, always remove your shoes and wash your feet. Not to comply with these religious rules, regardless of your own beliefs, is ungracious and will get you thrown out.

Because action shots often make the best photographs, and light is hard to predict far from your
familiar photo-hunting grounds, buy high-speed
film for travel photography. In strong light, use a
filter, except on ski vacations and in areas where
strong light is constant.

Always brace your camera firmly when shooting. Hold it with both hands, and steady your elbows against your body. Action shots, and shots in low light, warrant extra support — try bracing your whole body against a car or building. Hold your breath if necessary when pressing the shutter.

For my part, I travel not to go anywhere, but to go. I travel for travel's sake. The great affair is to move.

— R.L. Stevenson

The swiftest traveler is he who goes afoot.

— Thoreau

. . . .

. . . .

. . . .

. . . .

. . . .

. . . .

. . . .

. . . .

. . . .

. . . .

. . . .

. . . .

. . . .

. . . .

. . . .

. . . .

Taking pets along without calling ahead to warn your hotel can be risky. Many establishments in the U.S. allow pets, but in other cases you must make separate arrangements with a local kennel. Don't try to sneak your pet into the hotel or inn — this may cause unpleasant (and possibly expensive) repercussions.

. . . .

. . . .

. . . .

. . . .

. . . .

. . . .

. . . .

. . . .

. . . .

. . . .

. . . .

. . . .

*People in hotels strike no roots. The French phrase
for chronic hotel guests even says so: they are
called dwellers* sur la branche.

— Edward Verrall Lucas, 1926

Mountains are the earth's undecaying monuments.
— Hawthorne

Luxury dude ranches offer a full range of activities and entertainment, but if you plan to holiday on a real working ranch, be prepared to look after yourself if you choose not to help brand the calves. The same goes for any vacation on which yourself should you choose not to help brand the on a ranch, farm, or ship.

. . . .

. . . .

. . . .

. . . .

. . . .

. . . .

. . . .

. . . .

. . . .

. . . .

. . . .

. . . .

. . . .

. . . .

. . . .

Wales has more castles per square mile than any other European country. In 11,000 square miles, 400 intact or ruinous castles are found.

. . . .

. . . .

. . . .

. . . .

. . . .

. . . .

. . . .

. . . .

. . . .

. . . .

. . . .

. . . .

. . . .

. . . .

. . . .

. . . .

From the lone sheiling of the misty island
Mountains divide us, and the waste of seas—
Yet still the blood is strong, the heart is Highland,
And we in dreams behold the Hebrides.
—David Macbeth Moir, 1829

Resist the temptation to shoot photographs from a moving vehicle. Vibrations and the flashing scenery ignored by your selective vision will create blurry, disappointing shots.

When traveling on the road, look for a restaurant whose parking lot is full of local cars. This suggests a popular restaurant with a good reputation, rather than a roadside spot only servicing motorists.

Pack shoes closest to the hinge ends of your suit-case, so that they will be on the bottom when the suitcase is upright.

. . . .

. . . .

. . . .

. . . .

. . . .

. . . .

. . . .

. . . .

. . . .

. . . .

. . . .

. . . .

. . . .

. . . .

. . . .

I travel light; as light,
That is, as a man can travel who will
Still carry his body around because
Of its sentimental value.

— Christopher Fry, 1950

I want to travel in Europe...I know that I am only going to a graveyard, but it's a most precious graveyard.

— Dostoevsky

Happy he who like Ulysses has made a glorious voyage.

— Joachim du Bellay, 1559

. . . .
. . . .
. . . .
. . . .
. . . .
. . . .
. . . .
. . . .
. . . .
. . . .
. . . .
. . . .
. . . .
. . . .
. . . .
. . . .
. . . .

When traveling with children in a country or region where you are likely to encounter — and want to sample — unusual cuisine, give your children vitamin pills every day. In the case that they are unwilling to try unfamiliar foods, you will worry less about their being well nourished this way.

. . . .

. . . .

. . . .

. . . .

. . . .

. . . .

. . . .

. . . .

. . . .

. . . .

. . . .

. . . .

. . . .

TAKE THE BEST

SHILOH'S CURE.

Religious observances in some countries can mean disrupted service or tremendous crowds, so before planning an international trip, look into local holidays, feasts, fasts, and festivals. These celebrations may add greatly to your enjoyment of a trip, but they also can be exhausting.

O bright and violet-crowned and famed in song,
bulwark of Greece, famous Athens, divine city!
                                          —Pindar

Greece and Turkey, although similar in culture, are very hostile toward one another. A visa from one will not prevent entry into the other, but direct travel between the two is difficult, and accompanied by heavy taxes and surcharges. Furthermore, no official of either country will be forthcoming with information on how to travel to the other, so be sure you know exactly how to get from one to the other on your own, or travel between the two indirectly.

The severity of jet lag depends on the length of flight, the individual, and the direction of travel. Flying from east to west is harder on the system than flying from west to east. Therefore, if you plan to fly around the world, the cumulative jet lag will be much less if you fly to the east than if you fly to the west.

When scheduling a very long flight, such as New York to Sydney or Tokyo, choose one making as few stops as possible. The more time spent on the ground, the greater the chances of delays waiting for clearances, fueling, runways, etc.

*Soldiers, from the summit of yonder pyramids
forty centuries look down upon you.*

— Napoleon

. . . .

. . . .

. . . .

. . . .

. . . .

. . . .

. . . .

. . . .

. . . .

. . . .

. . . .

. . . .

. . . .

. . . .

. . . .

. . . .

I traveled among unknown men,
In lands beyond the sea;
Nor, England! did I know till then
What love I bore to thee.

— Wordsworth

Many areas of the world — particularly remote parts of Asia — have only recently opened up to tourism, and the sight of a Westerner is a novelty. Expect either unbridled curiosity accompanied by much touching and following, or thinly-veiled mistrust and hostility. In neither case are you in a position to complain, as your presence is unexpected, and possibly unprecedented.

. . . .

. . . .

. . . .

. . . .

. . . .

. . . .

. . . .

. . . .

. . . .

. . . .

. . . .

. . . .

. . . .

. . . .

The use of traveling is to regulate the imagination by reality, and instead of thinking how things may be, to see them as they are.

— Samuel Johnson

I have seen starry archipelagos! And islands
Whose raving skies are opened to the voyager:
Is it in these bottomless nights that you sleep,
   in exile
A million golden birds, O future Vigor?
                              — Arthur Rimbaud, 1871

. . . .

. . . .

. . . .

. . . .

. . . .

. . . .

. . . .

. . . .

. . . .

. . . .

. . . .

. . . .

. . . .

Beyond the Alps lies Italy.

—Livy

Objects which are usually the motives of our travels by land and by sea are often overlooked and neglected if they lie under our eye... We put off from time to time going and seeing what we know we have the opportunity of seeing when we please.
— Pliny the Younger

Classics which at home are drowsily read have a strange charm in a country inn, or in the transom of a merchant brig.

— Emerson

Moscow... now many strains are fusing in the one sound, for Russian hearts! What store of riches it imparts!

— Pushkin

Travel in Eastern Block countries is fraught with restrictions and regulations, but well worth the bother. Visas can be obtained for all except Albania, and hitchhiking is legal and very much encouraged by the governments. However, in many countries it is illegal to stay at private residences, and often local police must be reported to and asked permission of regarding many activities. If you are told that a town has "no facilities" for tourists, don't argue. This is a euphemism for off limits. No amount of complaining or bribing will allow you into a restricted town or region.

I found Rome a city of brick and left it a city of marble.

— Julius Caesar

Read up on the history and culture of the area you plan to visit. It might increase your enjoyment of the trip to read a novel that was written in the same village you will be visiting, or to seek out the birthplace of an historical figure you always admired. Chambers of Commerce and Tourist Boards can be helpful in supplying this kind of information.

. . . .

. . . .

. . . .

. . . .

. . . .

. . . .

. . . .

. . . .

. . . .

. . . .

. . . .

. . . .

. . . .

. . . .

Instead of planning your vacation around a particular area or event, try one inspired by an activity you enjoy. A tour of the gardens of the Deep South or the castles of France's Loire Valley, or a horseback trip through the Rockies might be more fun and engaging than a standard "sightseeing mission."

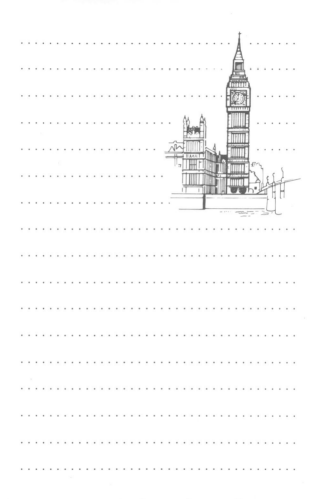

London, thou art the flower of Cities all.
—William Dunbar, 1465–1530

I always love to begin a journey on Sundays, because I shall have the prayers of the church to preserve all that travel by land, or by water.

— Swift

If you are traveling to one destination and plan to stay there for a while, pack dirty clothes instead of freshly cleaned and pressed garments, and send them out to be cleaned on arrival. Your clothes will end up looking fresher.

Ay, now I am in Arden; the more fool I: when I was at home, I was in a better place: but travellers must be content.

— Shakespeare

. . . .

. . . .

. . . .

. . . .

. . . .

. . . .

. . . .

. . . .

. . . .

. . . .

. . . .

. . . .

. . . .

. . . .

Traveling is a fool's paradise ... My giant goes with me wherever I go.

— Emerson

Led by my hand, he sauntered Europe round;
And gathered every vice on Christian ground.
— Pope

Upon arrival in an unfamiliar country or one which is experiencing civil unrest, check in with your consulate or embassy for anything you might need to know.

. . . .

. . . .

. . . .

. . . .

. . . .

. . . .

. . . .

. . . .

. . . .

. . . .

. . . .

. . . .

. . . .

. . . .

. . . .

O Rome! my country! city of the soul!

—Byron

Some of the most important, and best preserved, non-secular frescoes of 14th-century Italy were discovered in the Castello di Pomerio, in Como. While renovating the castle into a hotel, layers of centuries-old plaster were removed, revealing the perfectly preserved frescoes, which had been hidden for hundreds of years.

*As the Spanish proverb says, "He, who would
bring home the wealth of the Indies, must carry
the wealth of the Indies with him," so it is in traveling, a man must carry knowledge with him if he
would bring home knowledge.*

— Samuel Johnson

A traveler has a right to relate and embellish his adventures as he pleases, and it is very impolite to refuse that deference and applause they deserve.
—Rudolf Erich Raspe, 1785

Some countries, for a variety of reasons, simply do not want tourists. In some cases a lack of dependence on tourist dollars results in little need to put up with tourist-related problems, and in others, it is due to political or religious differences. The degree of difficulty in obtaining a visa indicates how much a country wants to keep you out, and if you do obtain one, don't expect to be treated very well once you arrive. Officials may be obstructive, and citizens suspicious or unwelcoming.

A Taiwanese visa will obstruct or prevent your entry into China, and a South African visa will keep you out of most Black African nations.

I have traveled a good deal in Concord.

— Thoreau

Take advantage whenever possible of discounts which apply to your and your family. Youth and student fares, family rates, and senior citizen discounts can comprise considerable savings on transportation and lodging expenses. Discounted rates also apply to many museums and other cultural institutions. Be sure to inform ticket and travel agents of your status with regard to these discounts.

Before you begin packing for your trip, make a list — don't just think about it. List-making can make the difference between a good and bad vacation. Go over the list often — determine your needs, which items are luxuries, and what can be removed from the list. Remember, all warm places can turn cool, and cool places can suddenly warm up. Be prepared for changes of weather, as well as a variety of social occasions. A sewing kit, guidebooks, and extra film are always good to have on hand.

. . . .

. . . .

. . . .

. . . .

. . . .

. . . .

. . . .

I stood in Venice on the Bridge of Sighs,
A palace and a prison on each hand.

— Byron

The great advantage of a hotel is that it's a refuge from home life.

— Shaw

The lower air pressure in airplane cabins can be tiring on a long flight. To minimize discomfort, loosen clothing and take off your shoes, and recline if possible. Smoking will magnify the effects of the pressurization, so resist smoking if you can. And on longer flights, avoid drinking much coffee or tea, as they cause dehydration and will make you more thirsty, and possibly give you a headache. In dry airplane air it is better to drink juice or soda.

My heart is warm with the friends I make,
And better friends I'll not be knowing;
Yet there isn't a train I wouldn't take,
No matter where it's going.
                              —Edna St. Vincent Millay

. . . .

. . . .

. . . .

. . . .

. . . .

. . . .

. . . .

. . . .

. . . .

. . . .

. . . .

. . . .

. . . .

. . . .

Bind us in time, O seasons clear, and awe.
O minstrel galleons of Carib fire,
Bequeath us to no earthly shore until
Is answered in the vortex of our grave
The sea's wide spindrift gaze toward paradise.
— Hart Crane, 1926

The excursion is the same when you go looking for your sorrow as when you go looking for your joy.

— Eudora Welty

May the countryside and the gliding valley streams content me. Lost to fame, let me love river and woodland.

— Virgil

Germany abounds in castles, monasteries, and royal hunting lodges which have been converted into hotels. For the most part, the accommodations are not as luxurious as their French counterparts; but the experience of staying in one of these hotels, some of which date back to the 11th century, makes up for the lack of plushness.

. . . .

. . . .

. . . .

. . . .

. . . .

. . . .

. . . .

. . . .

. . . .

. . . .

. . . .

. . . .

. . . .

In many Third World and in all Communist Bloc countries, authorities are very sensitive about photographers. Never attempt to photograph border crossings, military installations or personnel, trains, planes, anything which might make a developing country look "backward," or anything which is remotely governmental or police-oriented. To take photographs of such subjects is to risk having your film and/or camera confiscated, or even spending hours or days in police custody, accused of espionage.

They spell it Vinci and pronounce it Vinchy; for-eigners always spell better than they pronounce.
— Twain

Farewell to the Highlands, farewell to the North,
The birthplace of valor, the country of worth!
Wherever I wander, wherever I rove,
The hills of the Highlands forever I love.

— Burns

The sprinkled isles,
Lily on lily, that o'erlace the sea.

— Browning

Now spurs the lated traveler apace
To gain the timely inn.

— Shakespeare

This land is your land, this land is my land,
From California to the New York island,
From the redwood forest to the Gulf Stream
  waters,
This land was made for you and me.
                                    —Woody Guthrie

An airport x-ray machine which claims not to damage film won't—unless the same film is x-rayed several times. When on extended trips requiring many passages through airport security systems, process exposed film before you return home. For "there and back" trips, you needn't worry about your film.

To travel hopefully is a better thing than to arrive.
— R.L. Stevenson

. . . .
. . . .
. . . .
. . . .
. . . .
. . . .
. . . .
. . . .
. . . .
. . . .
. . . .
. . . .
. . . .
. . . .
. . . .
. . . .
. . . .

Setting out on the voyage to Ithaca
You must pray that the way be long,
Full of adventures and experiences.
— Constantine Peter Cavafy, 1911

Does the road wind uphill all the way?
Yes, to the very end.
Will the journey take the whole long day?
From morn to night, my friend.

— Christina Rossetti, 1861

*I love Vermont because of her hills and valleys,
her scenery and invigorating climate.*
— Calvin Coolidge

And on longer flights, avoid drinking much coffee or tea, as they cause dehydration and will make you more thirsty, and possibly give you a headache. In dry airplane air it is better to drink juice or soda.

. . . .

. . . .

. . . .

. . . .

. . . .

. . . .

. . . .

. . . .

. . . .

. . . .

. . . .

. . . .

. . . .

. . . .

Whenever possible, use a travel agent for air travel. An agent will find the most economical fares for you, at or lower than the cost of doing it yourself. Agents do not charge for their services, as they buy the tickets at a discount from the airline and sell them at a profit, so don't hesitate to avail yourself of this service. However, some agents will book you on an airline that gives them a larger discount, regardless of the economy to you. Check out all the options to be sure of a good value.

Not fare well,
But fare forward, voyagers.

—T.S. Eliot

Time Conversions

When it's 3 P.M. in New York:

    Honolulu — 10 A.M.

    Halifax — 4 P.M.

    Los Angeles* & San Francisco* — 12 noon

    Rio de Janeiro — 5 P.M.

    Denver* — 1 P.M.

    London — 8 P.M.

    Chicago* & Mexico City — 2 P.M.

    Berlin, Rome & Paris — 9 P.M.

    Moscow — 11 A.M. tomorrow

    Singapore — 3:30 A.M. tomorrow

    Manila — 4 A.M. tomorrow

    Sydney & Guam — 6 A.M. tomorrow

*One hour later during Daylight Savings Time.

Mileage Between Major U.S. Cities

New York to Boston, 206
New York to Philadelphia, 100
New York to Washington, D.C., 233
New York to Atlanta, 841
New York to Miami, 1308
New York to Chicago, 802
New York to St. Louis, 948
New York to Dallas, 1552
New York to Los Angeles, 2786
New York to San Francisco, 2934
Boston to Washington, D.C., 429
Boston to Chicago, 963
Boston to Los Angeles, 2979
Chicago to Washinton, D.C., 671

Chicago to Atlanta, 674
Chicago to Dallas, 917
Chicago to St. Louis, 289
Chicago to San Francisco, 2142
Chicago to Los Angeles, 2054
St. Louis to Dallas, 630
St. Louis to San Francisco, 2089
St. Louis to Los Angeles, 1845
Los Angeles to San Francisco, 379
Philadelphia to Washington, D.C., 133
Washington, D.C. to Atlanta, 608
Washington, D.C. to Miami, 1075
Atlanta to Miami, 655
Dallas to Miami, 1300

Converting Foreign Currencies*

Country	Local Currency	Approx. value of foreign currency in U.S. $
Austria	schilling = 100 groschen	1 schilling = $0.057
Brazil	cruzeiro = 100 centavos	1 cruzeiro = $0.002
Canada	dollar = 100 cents	1 dollar = $0.82
Denmark	krone = 100 ore	1 krone = $0.11
France	franc = 100 centimes	1 franc = $0.135
West Germany	deutsche mark = 100 pfennig	1 mark = $0.40
Great Britain	pound sterling = 100 new pence	1 pound = $1.56
Greece	drachma = 100 lepta	1 drachma = $0.012
Hong Kong	dollar = 100 cents	1 dollar = $0.145
Italy	lira = 100 centesimi	100 lira = $0.07
Japan	yen = 100 sen	100 yen = $0.43
Mexico	peso = 100 centavos	1 peso = $0.007
Spain	peseta = 100 centimos	1 peseta = $0.007
Switzerland	franc = 100 centimes	1 franc = $0.485

*Subject to change.

Average Temperatures Around the World
(in Fahrenheit degrees)

	JAN.	APR.	JULY	OCT.
Athens	48	60	81	67
Bahamas	72	75	82	80
Beijing	24	58	77	56
Copenhagen	32	42	62	48
Frankfurt	31	46	65	48
Geneva	29	47	65	48
Jerusalem	45	61	76	70
London	39	48	63	50
Madrid	41	53	74	56
Moscow	10	36	62	36
Paris	37	50	66	52
Rio de Janeiro	78	77	69	72
Rome	44	58	77	62
Tokyo	39	55	76	62